Edition Schott

Guitar Archive · Gitarren-Archiv

Johann Sebastian Bach

1685 – 1750

Suite No. 1

für Gitarre
for Guitar
BWV 1007

(Original: Violoncello solo)

Edited by / Herausgegeben von
John W. Duarte

GA 213
ISMN 979-0-2201-1642-1

www.schott-music.com

Mainz · London · Berlin · Madrid · New York · Paris · Prague · Tokyo · Toronto

The first edition of this arrangement (1965) has received at least three commercial recordings and very many concert performances. However successful, arrangements are nevertheless subject to evolution and they neither can nor should be regarded as definite 'for all time'. One's view of the text and of its translation to the instrument inevitably changes with time and, after 17 years, I felt it desirable to revise my original score. The original fingerings (by John Williams) have been changed only insofar as is necessary to adjust to changes in the text, mainly with regard to note-content and articulation.

Suggested interpretations of the ornaments are footnoted throughout. All the ornaments contained in Bach's autograph are retained and are denoted by the sign *tr*, which he used to cover all eventualities; others are added, in line with baroque practice, and are denoted only by their bracketed reference numbers. In this way the user may know which are original and which are not, and may choose whether or not to use the latter. It would be perfectly 'proper' practice to use only the original ornaments in playing each section for the first time, introducing the added ones on repeating.

John W. Duarte (1982)

Die erste Ausgabe (von 1965) der vorliegenden Bearbeitung ist bereits dreimal auf Schallplatte aufgenommen worden und wurde in vielen Konzerten benutzt. Auch eine erfolgreiche Bearbeitung ist nichtsdestoweniger einer Entwicklung unterworfen und kann und soll nicht als etwas Endgültiges betrachtet werden. Unumgänglicherweise ändert man seine Auffassung des Textes und seiner Umsetzbarkeit für das jeweilige Instrument im Lauf der Zeit, und nach 17 Jahren hatte ich das Bedürfnis die Partitur zu überarbeiten. Die Originalfingersätze (von John Williams) wurden nur dort geändert wo Anderungen im Text es notwendig erscheinen liessen, hauptsächlich im Hinblick auf Noteninhalt und Artikulation.

Vorschläge zur Ausführung sind jeweils in den Anmerkungen enthalten. Die in Bachs Autographie enthaltenen Verzierungen wurden beibehalten und durch das Zeichen *tr*, von Bach für verschiedene Ausführungsmöglichkeiten benutzt, gekennzeichnet; weitere Verzierungen wurden im Sinne barocker Aufführungspraxis eingefügt und sind lediglich durch eingeklammerte Nummern gekennzeichnet. Der Benützer kann so leicht feststellen ob Verzierungen im Original enthalten sind oder nicht, und ob er es vorzieht die letzteren anzuwenden. Es wäre im Rahmen der Aufführungspraxis durchaus akzeptabel beim ersten Durchspielen nur die Originalverzierungen zu benützen und die anderen bei der Wiederholung einzufügen.

John W. Duarte (1982)

Suite No. 1

BWV 1007

New edition, with revisions by
Revidierte Neuausgabe von
John W. Duarte

J. S. Bach

I Prelude

CV
II
½CII
½CVII
½CV
½CII
½CVII

II Allemande

½CII
½CII
(8)
CII
(9)
(10)
(11)
CII
(12)
½CII
CII
½CII
CII

III Courante

CII
CVI
(4)
CII
CII
CV
CII
(5)
CII
CII
(6)

IV Sarabande

V Minuet I
Minuet II

VI Gigue